Stories of Santa

Up on the Housetop
Jolly Old St. Nicholas

A STORYBOOK OF TWO BELOVED SANTA SONGS

Hallmark

to
Morgan

Grandma *from* Pixie

Up on the Housetop

BENJAMIN R. HANBY

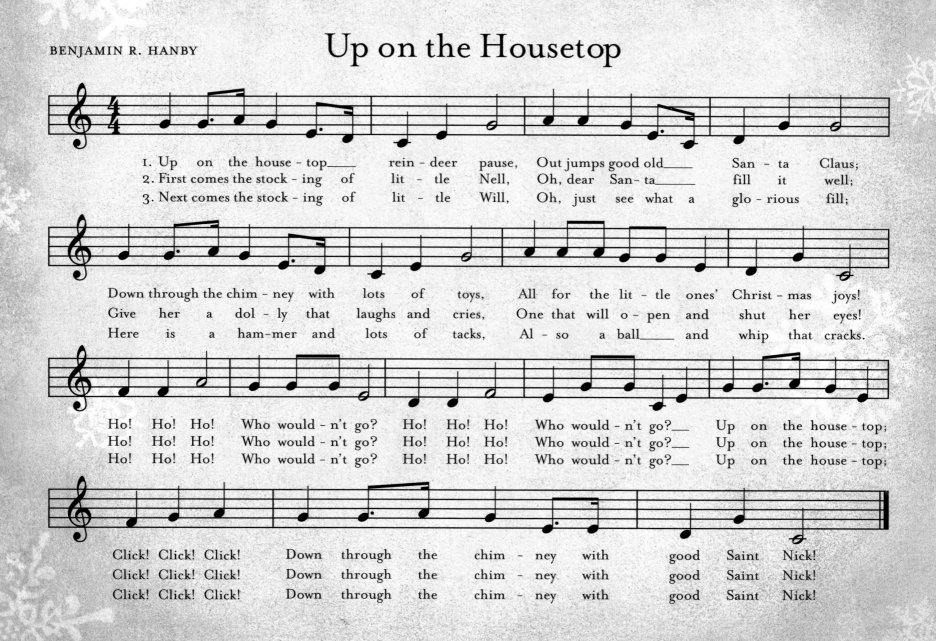

UP ON THE HOUSETOP

Up on the housetop reindeer pause,
Out jumps good old Santa Claus,
Down through the chimney with lots of toys,
All for the little ones' Christmas joys!

First comes the stocking of little Nell,
Oh, dear Santa, fill it well...

Give her a dolly that laughs and cries,
One that will open and shut her eyes!

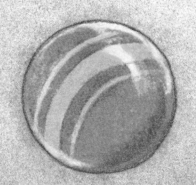

Next comes the stocking of little Will,
Oh, just see what a glorious fill...

Here is a hammer and lots of tacks,
Also a ball...and a whip that cracks.

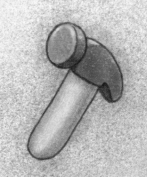

Ho! Ho! Ho!
Who wouldn't go?
Ho! Ho! Ho!
Who wouldn't go?

Up on the housetop...
Click! Click! Click!
Down through the chimney
with good Saint Nick.

Favorite gifts from Santa

_____
_____
_____
_____
_____
_____
_____
_____
_____
_____
_____
_____
_____

Christmas songs and stories we love

_____
_____
_____
_____
_____
_____
_____
_____
_____
_____
_____
_____
_____
_____
_____

The best part of Christmas

_____
_____
_____
_____
_____
_____
_____
_____
_____
_____
_____
_____
_____

SANTA AND ME

FAMILY PHOTOS

All I want for Christmas

_____
_____
_____
_____
_____
_____
_____
_____
_____
_____
_____
_____
_____
_____

Our best Christmas memories

_____
_____
_____
_____
_____
_____
_____
_____
_____
_____
_____
_____
_____
_____

Jolly Old Saint Nicholas

1. Jol - ly old Saint Ni - cho - las, Lean your ear this way!
2. When the clock is strik - ing twelve, When I'm fast a - sleep,
3. John - ny wants a pair of skates, Su - sy wants a sled.

Don't you tell a sin - gle soul What I'm going to say;
Down the chim - ney broad and black, With your pack you'll creep;
Nel - lie wants a pict - ure book, Yel - low, blue, and red.

Christ - mas Eve is com - ing soon; Now, my dear old man,
All the stock - ings you will find Hang - ing in a row;
Now I think I'll leave to you What to give the rest.

Whis - per what you'll bring to me; Tell me if you can.
Mine will be the short - est one, You'll be sure to know.
Choose for me, dear San - ta Claus, You will know the best.

JOLLY OLD SAINT NICHOLAS

Jolly old Saint Nicholas,
Lean your ear this way!
Don't you tell a single soul
What I'm going to say.

Christmas Eve is coming soon.
Now, my dear old man,
Whisper what you'll bring to me,
Tell me, if you can.

When the clock is striking twelve,
When I'm fast asleep,
Down the chimney, broad and black,
With your pack you'll creep.

All the stockings you will find
Hanging in a row.
Mine will be the shortest one,
You'll be sure to know.

Johnny wants a pair of skates.
Susy wants a sled.
Nellie wants a picture book,
Yellow, blue, and red.

Now I think I'll leave to you
What to give the rest.
Choose for me, dear Santa Claus,
You will know the best.